More MAKING THE GRADE · GRADE 3

EASY POPULAR PIECES FOR YOUNG PIANISTS. SELECTED AND ARRANGED BY JEr

Exclusive distributors:
Music Sales Limited
Newmarket Road, Bury St Edmunds, Suffolk IP33 3YB.
This book © Copyright 1999 Chester Music
Order No. CH61535
ISBN 0-7119-7686-4
Cover design and typesetting by Pemberton & Whitefoord
Music engraved by Jerry Lanning
Printed in the United Kingdom by
Caligraving Limited, Thetford, Norfolk

Chester Music

(A division of Music Sales Limited)
14-15 Berners Street, London W1T 3LJ.

INTRODUCTION

This collection of 15 popular tunes provides additional attractive teaching repertoire to complement the first books in the MAKING THE GRADE series. As with the previous books, the pieces have been carefully arranged and graded and the collection is made up of well-known material which pupils will enjoy. The standard of the pieces progresses from Associated Board Grade 3.

CONTENTS

SHEPHERD MOONS

Music by Enya & Nicky Ryan

Use *legato* pedal and keep your hands relaxed. Bring out the melody clearly.

SLOOP JOHN B

Traditional

The left hand has some interesting rhythms. Be sure to play them really accurately.

I'LL BE MISSING YOU

Words & music by Sting, T. Gaither & F. Evans

Play as smoothly as possible, particularly the introduction.
Change the pedal every bar as a rule.

THIS OLE HOUSE

Words & music by Stuart Hamblen

Practise the left hand until you can play it accurately without looking at the keys.
Don't play the repeated right hand crotchets too short.

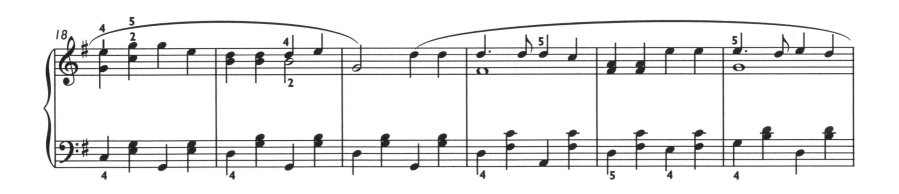

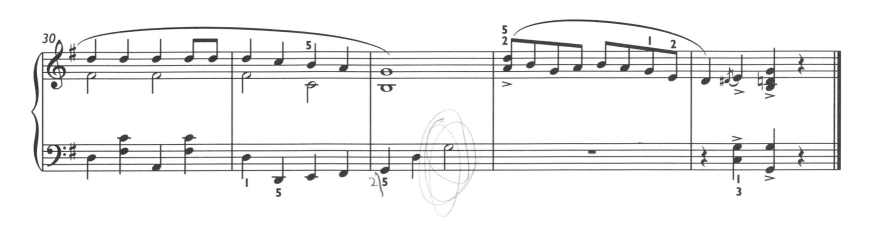

FÜR ELISE

Composed by Ludwig van Beethoven

The music should flow as smoothly as possible. Practise bars 12 to 17 with particular care,
so that the hands take over from each other without hesitation.

TRAGEDY

Words & music by Barry Gibb, Robin Gibb & Maurice Gibb

Practise the right hand alone from bar 13 until you are able to bring the tune out clearly.
Listen hard to the left hand in bars 11 and 12.

JUST THE WAY YOU ARE

Words & music by Billy Joel

Practise slowly enough to be aware of eight quavers in each bar
until you are sure of all the rhythms.

GOD ONLY KNOWS

Words & music by Brian Wilson & Tony Asher

Keep a very steady tempo with the left hand crotchet chords.

WITHOUT YOU

Words & music by Peter Ham & Tom Evans

Play all the quavers in as sustained a manner as possible.
A little rhythmic freedom is appropriate.

MICHELLE

Words & music by John Lennon & Paul McCartney

Bring out the melody clearly, taking care to play the other right hand notes more softly.
Watch out for the accidentals.

Moderately ♩ = 108

FERNANDO

Words & music by Benny Andersson, Stig Anderson & Bjorn Ulvaeus

Practise the right hand alone at first, trying for a good *legato* particularly in the upper voice.
If you have a small hand you may need to experiment with the fingering in bars 10 to 13.

WOMAN

Words & music by John Lennon

Take care with the fingering and try to play as *legato* as possible.

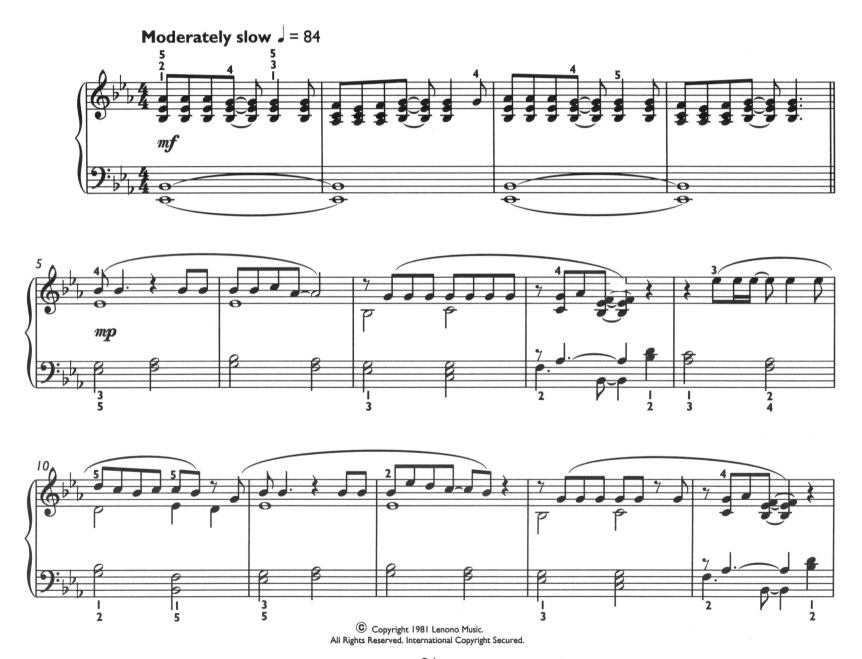

MASTER OF THE HOUSE

Music by Claude-Michel Schonberg, lyrics by Herbert Kretzmer
Original text by Alain Boublil & Jean-Marc Natel

Use little or no pedal and keep a very steady tempo.
The left hand quavers might be played *staccato* throughout.

THE SKYE BOAT SONG

Traditional

Bring out the left hand melody clearly at bar 25, playing the right hand very lightly.

MAMMA MIA

Words & music by Benny Andersson, Stig Anderson & Bjorn Ulvaeus

Keep the left hand quavers very steady, and don't let them thump.
The right hand should predominate.

Moderately bright ♩ = 108